Help with Times Tables

The times tables are printed at the back of the book to give some extra practice.
Here are some things to remember to help you learn and use your times tables.

1 **Two lots of three** means the same as **three lots of two**.

This means that **2 x 3** is the same as saying **3 x 2**.

2 There are lots of ways of writing and saying times tables.

Here are some ways of saying   3 x 2 = 6.

                      2 + 2 + 2 = 6;   3 lots of 2 are 6;

                      3 multiplied by 2 is 6;   3 times 2 equals 6.

3 **0 x** a number is always **0**.
For example,   0 x 2 = 0 because there are no lots of two.
                      2 x 0 = 0 because there are two lots of nothing.

4 **1 x** a number always leaves that number unchanged.
For example,   1 x 2 = 2 because there is one lot of 2.
                      1 x 100 = 100 because there is one lot of 100.

5 **10 x** a number means you move all the digits in the number one place to the left.
Fill the units column with a 0.

  H T U   H T U   H T U   H T U
    5 x 10 =   5 0   2 3 x 10 = 2 3 0
            ↑   ↑

6 **Double** means **x2**. **Twice** means **x2**.

7 A **multiple** is the answer you get when one number is multiplied by another:
1 x 3 = 3;   2 x 3 = 6;   3 x 3 = 9;   4 x 3 = 12;   5 x 3 = 15.
The first five multiples of 3 are 3, 6, 9, 12, 15.

8 A times table can share some of its multiples with another times table.

9 To help you learn your **x4** table, double your **x2** table.
2 x 2 = 4,   2 x 4 = 8   3 x 2 = 6,   3 x 4 = 12

10 How do you answer ☐ x 3 = 6?

This question is asking how many lots of 3 there are in 6.
To get the answer, divide 6 by 3. The answer is 2.

11 How do you answer 4 x ☐ = 12?

This question is asking 4 lots of which number are in 12.
To get the answer, divide 12 by 4. The answer is 3.

x0 table

Any number **x0** always gives the answer **0**.
This is because **x0** means **multiplied by nothing**
or **no lots of a number**.

Write the answers to the **x0** table here.

1 x 0 =	☐		6 x 0 =	☐
2 x 0 =	☐		7 x 0 =	☐
3 x 0 =	☐		8 x 0 =	☐
4 x 0 =	☐		9 x 0 =	☐
5 x 0 =	☐		10 x 0 =	☐

Write the answers to these **x0** questions.

5 x 0 =	☐		32 x 0 =	☐
1000 x 0 =	☐		54 x 0 =	☐

x1 table

Any number **x1** leaves that number unchanged.
This is because **x1** means **1 lot of that number.**

Write the answers to the **x1** table here.

1 x 1 =	☐		6 x 1 =	☐
2 x 1 =	☐		7 x 1 =	☐
3 x 1 =	☐		8 x 1 =	☐
4 x 1 =	☐		9 x 1 =	☐
5 x 1 =	☐		10 x 1 =	☐

Write the answers to these **x1** questions.

12 x 1 =	☐		48 x 1 =	☐
9 x 1 =	☐		2000 x 1 =	☐

Key Stage 1 Times Tables Book 1

Schofield & Sims

TIMES TABLES 1

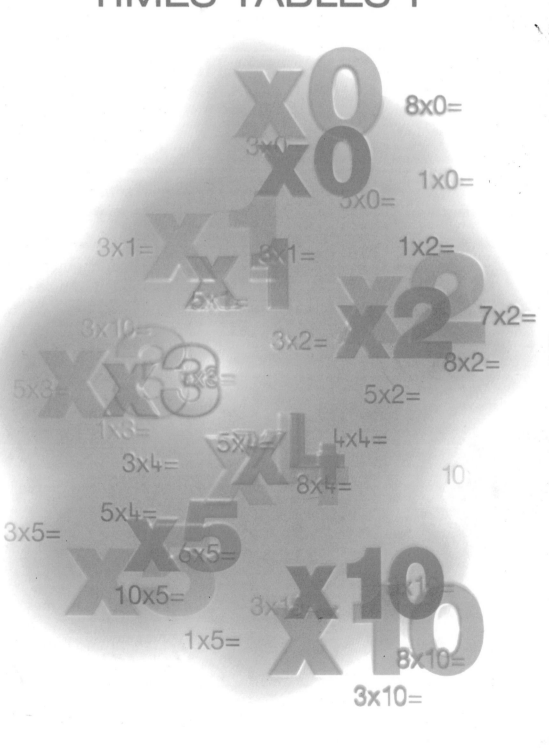

Name

Times Tables — Book 1

Cover design & illustration by Curve Creative, Bradford.

Printed by Wyndeham Gait Ltd., Grimsby

Schofield & Sims Limited
Huddersfield, England
Tel: 01484 607080 Fax: 01484 606815
E-mail: sales@schofieldandsims.co.uk

How to use this book

You will need:

- pen or pencil

- coloured pencils or felt tips

- spare paper

- stopwatch or a watch with a second hand to time yourself

To do the exercises:

1. Practise each times table by filling in the answers.

2. Mark the number grid with the answers to that times table.

3. Write and say the times table again.

4. Fill in the missing numbers in the times table.

5. Enjoy doing the times tables puzzles. These will help you to practise the times tables.

6. Try the timed tests. Keep a record of the date and how quickly you did each one. **Do one a day.**

Write the answers to the **x2** table here.

1 x 2 =

2 x 2 =

3 x 2 =

4 x 2 =

5 x 2 =

6 x 2 =

7 x 2 =

8 x 2 =

9 x 2 =

10 x 2 =

Look at this number grid. Colour all the answers to the **x2** table red.

1	2	3	4	5	6	7	8	9	10
11	12	13	14	15	16	17	18	19	20

These are the numbers in the **x2** table. They are the **multiples** of 2.

Are all the numbers in the **x2** table **odd** or **even**? _____

Colour the **x2** numbers red again. But this time keep **counting on** in **2s** until you reach **50**.

1	2	3	4	5	6	7	8	9	10
11	12	13	14	15	16	17	18	19	20
21	22	23	24	25	26	27	28	29	30
31	32	33	34	35	36	37	38	39	40
41	42	43	44	45	46	47	48	49	50

Write the **x2** table here.

☐	X	☐	=	☐
☐	X	☐	=	☐
☐	X	☐	=	☐
☐	X	☐	=	☐
☐	X	☐	=	☐
☐	X	☐	=	☐
☐	X	☐	=	☐
☐	X	☐	=	☐
☐	X	☐	=	☐
☐	X	☐	=	☐

Fill in the missing numbers in the **x2** table in the correct order.

1	X	☐	=	2
☐	X	2	=	☐
3	X	☐	=	☐
☐	X	2	=	8
☐	X	☐	=	☐
6	X	2	=	☐
7	X	2	=	☐
☐	X	2	=	☐
☐	X	2	=	18
☐	X	☐	=	☐

Fun at the fair

Count on in **2s** to join the dots. Start at 20.

Count **back** in **2s** to join the dots. Start at 20.

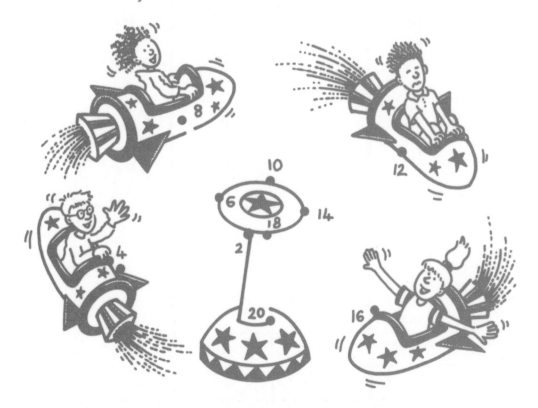

Record Breakers

How quickly can you do these tests?
Use a stopwatch and write the answers on spare paper.
Take 1 second off your time for every question you get **right**.
Add 3 seconds onto your time for every question you get **wrong**.

You will score better by being ACCURATE rather than FAST.

BUILD SPEED UP GRADUALLY while still trying to get all the answers right!!

Where you see ? this is the answer you need to give.

Keep a record of your times for each test here.

Do one test a day.

Test 1	Test 2	Test 3
2 x ? = 4	2 x ? = 0	? x 2 = 8
5 x 2 = ?	3 x ? = 0	? x 1 = 10
? x 2 = 12	3 x ? = 6	? x 2 = 0
3 x ? = 6	8 x ? = 8	? x 2 = 16
8 x ? = 16	8 x ? = 0	? x 1 = 7
4 x 2 = ?	8 x ? = 16	? x 1 = 8
? x 2 = 10	7 x ? = 7	? x 2 = 20
9 x 2 = ?	9 x ? = 18	? x 1 = 0
? x 2 = 14	5 x ? = 10	? x 2 = 18
10 x 2 = ?	4 x ? = 4	? x 2 = 4

Date	Time	Date	Time	Date	Time

 **table**

Write the answers to the **x3** table here.

1 x 3 = ☐

2 x 3 = ☐

3 x 3 = ☐

4 x 3 = ☐

5 x 3 = ☐

6 x 3 = ☐

7 x 3 = ☐

8 x 3 = ☐

9 x 3 = ☐

10 x 3 = ☐

Look at this number grid.
Colour all the answers to
the **x3** table purple.

1	2	3	4	5	6	7	8	9	10
11	12	13	14	15	16	17	18	19	20
21	22	23	24	25	26	27	28	29	30

These are the numbers in the **x3** table. They are the **multiples of 3.**

Can you see a pattern on the number grid?

Colour the **x3** numbers
purple again.
Keep **counting on** in **3s**
until you reach **60.**

Does the pattern change
or stay the same?

_____

1	2	3	4	5	6	7	8	9	10
11	12	13	14	15	16	17	18	19	20
21	22	23	24	25	26	27	28	29	30
31	32	33	34	35	36	37	38	39	40
41	42	43	44	45	46	47	48	49	50
51	52	53	54	55	56	57	58	59	60

Write the **x3** table here.

☐	x	☐	=	☐
☐	x	☐	=	☐
☐	x	☐	=	☐
☐	x	☐	=	☐
☐	x	☐	=	☐
☐	x	☐	=	☐
☐	x	☐	=	☐
☐	x	☐	=	☐
☐	x	☐	=	☐
☐	x	☐	=	☐

Fill in the missing numbers in the **x3** table in the correct order.

1	x	☐	=	3
☐	x	3	=	6
3	x	3	=	☐
☐	x	3	=	12
☐	x	☐	=	15
6	x	3	=	☐
7	x	☐	=	21
☐	x	3	=	☐
☐	x	3	=	27
10	x	☐	=	☐

Jigsaw Jumble

Write the answers to these times tables questions.
Join the puzzle pieces that give the same answers.

2 x 1 = ☐

2 x 3 = ☐

3 x 2 = ☐

1 x 2 = ☐

4 x 2 = ☐

5 x 2 = ☐

2 x 5 = ☐

6 x 3 = ☐

10 x 2 = ☐

2 x 10 = ☐

8 x 2 = ☐

9 x 2 = ☐

2 x 9 = ☐

2 x 8 = ☐

3 x 6 = ☐

2 x 4 = ☐

Record Breakers

How quickly can you do these tests?
Use a stopwatch and write the answers on spare paper.
Take 1 second off your time for every question you get **right**.
Add 3 seconds onto your time for every question you get **wrong**.

You will score better by being ACCURATE rather than FAST.

BUILD SPEED UP GRADUALLY while still trying to get all the answers right!!

Where you see ? this is the answer you need to give.

Test 1	Test 2	Test 3
2 x ? = 6	8 x ? = 24	? x 2 = 0
5 x ? = 15	3 x ? = 9	? x 3 = 24
? x 3 = 12	3 x ? = 27	? x 1 = 3
3 x ? = 9	4 x ? = 8	? x 3 = 15
8 x ? = 24	10 x ? = 0	? x 3 = 9
7 x 3 = ?	6 x ? = 18	? x 2 = 4
? x 3 = 27	7 x ? = 21	? x 3 = 30
1 x 3 = ?	9 x ? = 9	? x 3 = 27
? x 3 = 18	5 x ? = 10	? x 1 = 9
10 x 3 = ?	8 x ? = 16	? x 3 = 12

Keep a record of your times for each test here.

Do one test a day.

Date	Time	Date	Time	Date	Time

Write the answers to the **x4** table here.

1 x 4 = ☐

2 x 4 = ☐

3 x 4 = ☐

4 x 4 = ☐

5 x 4 = ☐

6 x 4 = ☐

7 x 4 = ☐

8 x 4 = ☐

9 x 4 = ☐

10 x 4 = ☐

Look at this number grid. Colour all the answers to the **x4** table yellow.

1	2	3	4	5	6	7	8	9	10
11	12	13	14	15	16	17	18	19	20
21	22	23	24	25	26	27	28	29	30
31	32	33	34	35	36	37	38	39	40

These are the **multiples of 4.**

Now colour all the **multiples of 2** in red.

Which numbers are multiples of both **2** and **4?**

☐ ☐ ☐ ☐ ☐

☐ ☐ ☐ ☐ ☐

The shared multiples of **2** and **4** are coloured orange on your grid.

Write the **x4** table here.

☐	x	☐	=	☐
☐	x	☐	=	☐
☐	x	☐	=	☐
☐	x	☐	=	☐
☐	x	☐	=	☐
☐	x	☐	=	☐
☐	x	☐	=	☐
☐	x	☐	=	☐
☐	x	☐	=	☐
☐	x	☐	=	☐

Fill in the missing numbers in the **x4** table in the correct order.

1	x	☐	=	4
☐	x	4	=	☐
3	x	☐	=	☐
☐	x	☐	=	16
5	x	☐	=	20
6	x	4	=	☐
7	x	☐	=	28
☐	x	4	=	☐
9	x	4	=	☐
☐	x	☐	=	40

Times Tables

x0
x1
x2
x3
x4
x5
x10

Key Stage 1 (England & Wales)
Mathematics 5-14 Level B (Scotland)

Book

1

ANSWERS

p4. The answers to the x0 table are 0. Any number multiplied by 0 gives the answer 0.
The answers to the x1 table are 1, 2, 3, 4, 5, 6, 7, 8, 9, 10.
12 x 1 = 12; 48 x 1 = 48; 9 x 1 = 9; 2000 x 1 = 2000.

p5. The answers to the x2 table are 2, 4, 6, 8, 10, 12, 14, 16, 18, 20.
These numbers should be coloured on the first number grid.
All the multiples of 2 are even.
You should colour the following squares on the second number grid:
2, 4, 6, 8, 10, 12, 14, 16, 18, 20, 22, 24, 26, 28, 30, 32, 34, 36, 38, 40, 42, 44, 46, 48, 50.

p6. The x2 table is: 1 x 2 = 2; 2 x 2 = 4; 3 x 2 = 6; 4 x 2 = 8; 5 x 2 = 10; 6 x 2 = 12; 7 x 2 = 14;
8 x 2 = 16; 9 x 2 = 18; 10 x 2 = 20.
The x2 table should be filled in with the numbers that are **bold**.
1 x 2 = 2; **2** x 2 = **4**; 3 x 2 = 6; **4** x 2 = **8**; **5** x 2 = **10**; 6 x 2 = 12; 7 x 2 = **14**; 8 x 2 = **16**;
9 x 2 = 18; 10 x 2 = **20**.

p7. Count on in twos to draw a dodgem car.
Count back in twos to draw a fairground ride.

p8. The answers you need to give are:
Remember:
? x 3 = 6 means how many lots of 3 make 6?
To get the answer divide 6 by 3.
6 ÷ 3 = 2

4 x ? = 12 means how many lots of 4 make 12?
To get the answer divide 12 by 4.
12 ÷ 4 = 3

Test 1	Test 2	Test 3
2	0	4
10	0	10
6	2	0
2	1	8
2	0	7
8	2	8
5	1	10
18	2	0
7	2	9
20	1	2

p9. The answers to the x3 table are 3, 6, 9, 12, 15, 18, 21, 24, 27, 30.
These numbers should be coloured on the first number grid.
You should colour the following squares on the second number grid:
3, 6, 9, 12, 15, 18, 21, 24, 27, 30, 33, 36, 39, 42, 45, 48, 51, 54, 57, 60.
The pattern is diagonal and remains the same.

p10. The x3 table is 1 x 3 = 3; 2 x 3 = 6; 3 x 3 = 9; 4 x 3 = 12; 5 x 3 = 15; 6 x 3 = 18;
7 x 3 = 21; 8 x 3 = 24; 9 x 3 = 27; 10 x 3 = 30.
The x3 table should be filled in with the numbers that are **bold**.
1 x 3 = 3; **2** x 3 = **6**; 3 x 3 = **9**; **4** x 3 = 12; **5** x 3 = 15; 6 x 3 = **18**; 7 x 3 = 21; 8 x 3 = **24**;
9 x 3 = 27; 10 x **3** = **30**.

p11. Join 2 x 1 = 2 to 1 x 2 = 2; 3 x 2 = 6 to 2 x 3 = 6; 4 x 2 = 8 to 2 x 4 = 8; 2 x 5 = 10 to 5 x 2 = 10;
10 x 2 = 20 to 2 x 10 = 20; 8 x 2 = 16 to 2 x 8 = 16; 2 x 9 = 18 to 9 x 2 = 18; 3 x 6 = 18 to 6 x 3 = 18.

p12. The answers you need to give are:
Remember:
? x 3 = 9 means how many lots of 3 make 9?
To get the answer divide 9 by 3.
9 ÷ 3 = 3

5 x ? = 10 means how many lots of 5 make 10?
To get the answer divide 10 by 5.
10 ÷ 5 = 2

Test 1	Test 2	Test 3
3	3	0
3	3	8
4	9	3
3	2	5
3	0	3
21	3	2
9	3	10
3	1	9
6	2	9
30	2	4

p13. The answers to the x4 table are 4, 8, 12, 16, 20, 24, 28, 32, 36, 40.
You should colour the following on the number grid in yellow:
4, 8, 12, 16, 20, 24, 28, 32, 36, 40.
You should colour the multiples of 2 red:
2, 4, 6, 8, 10, 12, 14, 16, 18, 20, 22, 24, 26, 28, 30, 32, 34, 36, 38, 40
The shared multiples of 2 and 4 are 4, 8, 12, 16, 20, 24, 28, 32, 36, 40.

p14. The x4 table is 1 x 4 = 4; 2 x 4 = 8; 3 x 4 = 12; 4 x 4 = 16; 5 x 4 =20; 6 x 4 = 24;
7 x 4 = 28; 8 x 4 = 32; 9 x 4 = 36; 10 x 4 = 40.
The x4 table should be filled in with the numbers that are **bold**.
1 x 4 = 4; **2 x 4 = 8**; 3 x 4 = 12; 4 x 4 = 16; 5 x 4 = 20; 6 x 4 = **24**; 7 x 4 = 28;
8 x 4 = 32; 9 x 4 = **36**; 10 x 4 = 40.

p15. There are 10 horses.
There are 40 legs. 10 x 4 = 40 legs
There are 10 tails. 10 x 1 = 10
There are 20 eyes. 10 x 2 = 20
There are 30 spots. 10 x 3 = 30.

p16. The answers you need to give are:
Remember:
 ? x 4 = 32 means how many lots of 4 make 32?
To get the answer divide 32 by 4.
32 ÷ 4 = 8

9 x ? = 27 means how many lots of 9 make 27?
To get the answer divide 27 by 9.
27 ÷ 9 = 3

Test 1	Test 2	Test 3
4	3	7
4	1	3
3	4	2
6	2	4
8	4	4
4	3	6
36	2	10
28	3	10
8	4	8
40	3	10

p17. The answers to the x5 table are: 5, 10, 15, 20, 25, 30, 35, 40, 45, 50.
You should colour the squares: 5, 10, 15, 20, 25, 30, 35, 40, 45, 50.
The multiples of 5 always end in a **5** or a **0**.

p18. The x5 table is 1 x 5 = 5; 2 x 5 = 10; 3 x 5 = 15; 4 x 5 = 20; 5 x 5 = 25; 6 x 5 = 30; 7 x 5 = 35;
8 x 5 = 40; 9 x 5 = 45; 10 x 5 = 50.
The x5 table should be filled in with the numbers that are in **bold**.
1 x 5 = 5; 2 x 5 = **10**; **3 x 5 = 15**; 4 x 5 = 20; 5 x 5 = **25**; 6 x 5 = **30**; 7 x 5 =35; **8 x 5 = 40**;
9 x 5 = 45; 10 x 5 = 50.

p19. The roller-coaster numbers should be joined in this order:
6, 20, 10, 0, 14, 24, 16, 50, 35, 30, 32, 27, 28, 40, 3, 45, 4, 36, 25, 12, 18, 21, 1, 2, 9.

p20. The answers you need to give are:
Remember:
 ? x 5 = 5 means how many lots of 5 make 5?
To get the answer divide 5 by 5.
5 ÷ 5 = 1

9 x ? = 27 means how many lots of 9 make 27?
To get the answer divide 27 by 9.
27 ÷ 9 = 3.

Test 1	Test 2	Test 3
5	3	10
10	5	8
3	4	3
4	4	5
30	4	4
8	3	9
45	2	7
35	3	4
1	4	6
10	3	9

p21. The answers to the x10 table are: 10, 20, 30, 40, 50, 60, 70, 80, 90, 100.
You should colour the squares 10, 20, 30, 40, 50, 60, 70, 80, 90, 100 yellow.
The multiples of 10 always end in a **0**.
The multiples of 5 are: 5, 10, 15, 20, 25, 30, 35, 40, 45, 50, 55, 60, 65, 70, 75, 80, 85, 90, 95, 100.
All the multiples of 10 are also multiples of 5: 10, 20, 30, 40, 50, 60, 70, 80, 90, 100.
5 and 10 share these multiples over 50: 60, 70, 80, 90, 100.

p22. The x10 table is: 1 x 10 = 10; 2 x 10 = 20; 3 x 10 = 30; 4 x 10 = 40; 5 x 10 = 50; 6 x 10 = 60;
7 x 10 = 70; 8 x 10 = 80; 9 x 10 = 90; 10 x 10 = 100.
The x10 table should be filled in with the numbers that are in **bold**.
1 x 10 = **10**; 2 x 10 = **20**; 3 x 10 = **30**; 4 x 10 = **40**; 5 x 10 = **50**; 6 x 10 = **60**;
7 x **10** = 70; 8 x 10 = **80**; 9 x **10** = 90; **10** x 10 = 100.

p23. Double £2 = £4; Twice £10 = £20; Twice £5 = £10; Double £4 = £8;
3 x £5 = £15; 10 x £10 = £100; 6 times £5 = £30; 8 times £3 = £24;
3 times 2p = 6p; 10 times 5p = 50p; 6p multiplied by 4 = 24p;
9 lots of 3p = 27p; 8p multiplied by 10 = 80p; 7 lots of 1p = 7p.

p24-25.

Test 1	Test 2	Test 3	Test 4
0	2	30	7
6	4	70	9
6	4	45	8
0	16	25	2
9	12	20	3
2	16	20	10
9	36	40	4
0	14	40	3
30	40	30	8
12	18	10	8
0	24	15	4
18	0	100	6

Test 5	Test 6	Test 7	Test 8
3	2	3	3
4	0	3	2
10	3	5	10
0	3	0	3
5	6	1	2
5	2	10	10
3	5	5	4
3	4	1	0
1	5	5	1
3	8	5	4
5	10	10	0
4	9	7	1

Test 9	Test 10	Test 11	Test 12
4	10	10	10
9	7	5	7
3	5	5	4
8	6	10	10
2	10	3	9
8	1	3	4
0	2	4	2
9	4	4	2
1	3	2	8
9	7	2	9
0	10	4	7
9	10	5	9

Merry-go-round!

How many horses are there altogether? ☐

How many legs are there altogether? ☐

10 x 4 = ☐

How many tails are there altogether? ☐

10 x 1 = ☐

How many eyes are there altogether? ☐

10 x 2 = ☐

How many spots are there altogether? ☐

10 x 3 = ☐

Record Breakers

How quickly can you do these tests?
Use a stopwatch and write the answers on spare paper.
Take 1 second off your time for every question you get **right**.
Add 3 seconds onto your time for every question you get **wrong**.

You will score better by being **ACCURATE** rather than FAST.

BUILD SPEED UP GRADUALLY while still trying to get all the answers right!!

Where you see ? this is the answer you need to give.

Test 1	Test 2	Test 3
1 x ? = 4	2 x ? = 6	? x 4 = 28
5 x ? = 20	3 x ? = 3	? x 3 = 9
? x 4 = 12	3 x ? = 12	? x 2 = 4
? x 4 = 24	8 x ? = 16	? x 3 = 12
2 x 4 = ?	8 x ? = 32	? x 4 = 16
? x 4 = 16	8 x ? = 24	? x 3 = 18
9 x 4 = ?	7 x ? = 14	? x 2 = 20
7 x 4 = ?	9 x ? = 27	? x 3 = 30
? x 4 = 32	5 x ? = 20	? x 4 = 32
10 x 4 = ?	4 x ? = 12	? x 4 = 40

Keep a record of your times for each test here.

Do one test a day.

Date	Time	Date	Time	Date	Time

 **table**

Write the answers to the **x5** table here.

1 x 5 = [ ]

2 x 5 = [ ]

3 x 5 = [ ]

4 x 5 = [ ]

5 x 5 = [ ]

6 x 5 = [ ]

7 x 5 = [ ]

8 x 5 = [ ]

9 x 5 = [ ]

10 x 5 = [ ]

Look at this number grid. Colour all the answers to the **x5** table blue.

1	2	3	4	5	6	7	8	9	10
11	12	13	14	15	16	17	18	19	20
21	22	23	24	25	26	27	28	29	30
31	32	33	34	35	36	37	38	39	40
41	42	43	44	45	46	47	48	49	50

These are the **multiples of 5.**

The multiples of 5 always end in a [ ] or a [ ] ?

Write the **x5** table here.

☐	x	☐	=	☐
☐	x	☐	=	☐
☐	x	☐	=	☐
☐	x	☐	=	☐
☐	x	☐	=	☐
☐	x	☐	=	☐
☐	x	☐	=	☐
☐	x	☐	=	☐
☐	x	☐	=	☐
☐	x	☐	=	☐

Fill in the missing numbers in the **x5** table in the correct order.

☐	x	5	=	5
2	x	5	=	☐
☐	x	5	=	☐
☐	x	☐	=	20
5	x	5	=	☐
6	x	5	=	☐
7	x	☐	=	35
☐	x	5	=	☐
9	x	☐	=	45
☐	x	☐	=	50

Roller-coaster ride

Answer these times tables questions. Then use your answers **in order** to join the dots.

2 x 3 = [   ]

4 x 5 = [   ]

2 x 5 = [   ]

0 x 1 = [   ]

7 x 2 = [   ]

8 x 3 = [   ]

4 x 4 = [   ]

10 x 5 = [   ]

7 x 5 = [   ]

10 x 3 = [   ]

8 x 4 = [   ]

9 x 3 = [   ]

7 x 4 = [   ]

10 x 4 = [   ]

3 x 1 = [   ]

9 x 5 = [   ]

2 x 2 = [   ]

9 x 4 = [   ]

5 x 5 = [   ]

4 x 3 = [   ]

9 x 2 = [   ]

7 x 3 = [   ]

1 x 1 = [   ]

2 x 1 = [   ]

3 x 3 = [   ]

19

Record Breakers

How quickly can you do these tests?
Use a stopwatch and write the answers on spare paper.
Take 1 second off your time for every question you get **right**.
Add 3 seconds onto your time for every question you get **wrong**.

You will score better by being ACCURATE rather than FAST.

BUILD SPEED UP GRADUALLY while still trying to get all the answers right!!

Where you see ? this is the answer you need to give.

Test 1	Test 2	Test 3
5 x ? = 25	5 x ? = 15	? x 5 = 50
2 x 5 = ?	3 x ? = 15	? x 4 = 32
? x 5 = 15	6 x ? = 24	? x 2 = 6
? x 5 = 20	9 x ? = 36	? x 4 = 20
6 x 5 = ?	4 x ? = 16	? x 5 = 20
? x 5 = 40	8 x ? = 24	? x 2 = 18
9 x 5 = ?	7 x ? = 14	? x 5 = 35
7 x 5 = ?	9 x ? = 27	? x 3 = 12
? x 5 = 5	5 x ? = 20	? x 5 = 30
? x 5 = 50	4 x ? = 12	? x 3 = 27

Keep a record of your times for each test here.

Do one test a day.

Date	Time	Date	Time	Date	Time

x10 table

Write the answers to the **x10** table here.

1 x 10 = ☐   6 x 10 = ☐

2 x 10 = ☐   7 x 10 = ☐

3 x 10 = ☐   8 x 10 = ☐

4 x 10 = ☐   9 x 10 = ☐

5 x 10 = ☐   10 x 10 = ☐

Look at this number grid. Colour all the answers to the **x10** table yellow.

1	2	3	4	5	6	7	8	9	10
11	12	13	14	15	16	17	18	19	20
21	22	23	24	25	26	27	28	29	30
31	32	33	34	35	36	37	38	39	40
41	42	43	44	45	46	47	48	49	50
51	52	53	54	55	56	57	58	59	60
61	62	63	64	65	66	67	68	69	70
71	72	73	74	75	76	77	78	79	80
81	82	83	84	85	86	87	88	89	90
91	92	93	94	95	96	97	98	99	100

These are the **multiples of 10.**
The multiples of 10 always end in a ☐ ?

Now colour the **multiples of 5** in blue. Keep counting on in 5s up to 100.
Which multiples do **10** and **5** share?

_____

Which multiples over 50 do 5 and 10 share? _____
(**REMEMBER,** the **x5** table always ends in a **5** or a **0.**)

Write the **x10** table here.

☐ x ☐ = ☐
☐ x ☐ = ☐
☐ x ☐ = ☐
☐ x ☐ = ☐
☐ x ☐ = ☐
☐ x ☐ = ☐
☐ x ☐ = ☐
☐ x ☐ = ☐
☐ x ☐ = ☐
☐ x ☐ = ☐

Fill in the missing numbers in the **x10** table in the correct order.

1 x 10 = ☐
☐ x 10 = 20
☐ x 10 = ☐
4 x ☐ = 40
☐ x 10 = ☐
6 x 10 = ☐
7 x ☐ = 70
☐ x 10 = ☐
9 x ☐ = 90
☐ x ☐ = 100

Money, money, money,

Use the times tables facts that you already know
to solve these problems.

Mr Costalot is putting all his prices up on his cake stall.
Write the new price in the box.

Double £2 = [ ]   **Twice £10 =** [ ]

Twice £5 = [ ]   **Double £4 =** [ ]

Mrs Costalot-More is putting her prices up by even more.
Write the new price in the box.

3 x £5 = [ ]   **10 x £10 =** [ ]

6 times £5 = [ ]   **8 times £3 =** [ ]

What are the new prices?

3 times 2p = [ ]   **10 times 5p =** [ ]

6p multiplied by 4 = [ ]   **9 lots of 3p =** [ ]

8p multiplied by 10 = [ ]   **7 lots of 1p =** [ ]

More Record Breakers

Using all the times table facts in this book, how quickly can you do these tests?
Again, use a stopwatch and write the answers on spare paper.
There are more questions in each test so you'll really have to try hard.
Take 2 seconds off your time for every question you get **right**.
But this time **add 5 seconds onto** your time for every question you get **wrong**.

You will score better by being ACCURATE rather than FAST.

BUILD SPEED UP GRADUALLY while still trying to get all the answers right!!

Where you see ? this is the answer you need to give.

Test 1	Test 2	Test 3	Test 4
0 x 3 = ?	1 x 2 = ?	6 x 5 = ?	? x 5 = 35
6 x 1 = ?	1 x 4 = ?	7 x 10 = ?	? x 2 = 18
2 x 3 = ?	2 x 2 = ?	9 x 5 = ?	? x 4 = 32
1 x 0 = ?	4 x 4 = ?	5 x 5 = ?	? x 10 = 20
3 x 3 = ?	3 x 4 = ?	2 x 10 = ?	? x 3 = 9
2 x 1 = ?	8 x 2 = ?	4 x 5 = ?	? x 4 = 40
9 x 1 = ?	9 x 4 = ?	8 x 5 = ?	? x 3 = 12
10 x 0 = ?	7 x 2 = ?	4 x 10 = ?	? x 4 = 12
10 x 3 = ?	10 x 4 = ?	3 x 10 = ?	? x 5 = 40
4 x 3 = ?	9 x 2 = ?	2 x 5 = ?	? x 10 = 80
5 x 0 = ?	6 x 4 = ?	3 x 5 = ?	? x 1 = 4
6 x 3 = ?	0 x 4 = ?	10 x 10 = ?	? x 3 = 18

Keep a record of your times for each test here.

Do one test a day.

Date	Time	Date	Time	Date	Time	Date	Time

Even More Record Breakers

Using all the times table facts in this book, how quickly can you do these tests?
Again, use a stopwatch and write the answers on spare paper.
There are more questions in each test so you'll really have to try hard.
Take 2 seconds off your time for every question you get **right**.
But this time **add 5 seconds onto** your time for every question you get **wrong**.

You will score better by being ACCURATE rather than FAST.

BUILD SPEED UP GRADUALLY while still trying to get all the answers right!!

Where you see ? this is the answer you need to give.

Keep a record of your times for each test here

Do one test a day.

Test 5	Test 6	Test 7	Test 8
5 x ? = 15	? x 2 = 4	? x 3 = 9	6 x ? = 18
4 x ? = 16	4 x ? = 0	? x 4 = 12	7 x ? = 14
10 x ? = 100	? x 2 = 6	? x 4 = 20	6 x ? = 60
? x 5 = 0	7 x ? = 21	? x 5 = 0	7 x ? = 21
? x 4 = 20	? x 4 = 24	? x 1 = 1	6 x ? = 12
8 x ? = 40	4 x ? = 8	? x 2 = 20	7 x ? = 70
7 x ? = 21	? x 10 = 50	? x 5 = 25	6 x ? = 24
9 x ? = 27	3 x ? = 12	? x 10 = 10	7 x ? = 0
? x 5 = 5	6 x ? = 30	? x 2 = 10	6 x ? = 6
10 x ? = 30	? x 2 = 16	? x 3 = 15	7 x ? = 28
9 x ? = 45	9 x ? = 90	? x 10 = 100	6 x ? = 0
2 x ? = 8	? x 3 = 27	? x 5 = 35	7 x ? = 7

Date	Time	Date	Time	Date	Time	Date	Time

Test 9	Test 10	Test 11	Test 12
8 x ? = 32	? x 5 = 50	3 x ? = 30	? x 4 = 40
? x 5 = 45	? x 5 = 35	5 x ? = 25	? x 5 = 35
9 x ? = 27	? x 4 = 20	3 x ? = 15	? x 4 = 16
? x 3 = 24	? x 3 = 18	8 x ? = 80	? x 2 = 20
9 x ? = 18	? x 10 = 100	8 x ? = 24	? x 2 = 18
? x 2 = 16	? x 2 = 2	4 x ? = 12	? x 5 = 20
8 x ? = 0	? x 4 = 8	9 x ? = 36	? x 3 = 6
? x 10 = 90	? x 2 = 8	7 x ? = 28	? x 5 = 10
8 x ? = 8	? x 3 = 9	4 x ? = 8	? x 3 = 24
? x 4 = 36	? x 4 = 28	6 x ? = 12	? x 1 = 9
9 x ? = 0	? x 3 = 30	3 x ? = 12	? x 3 = 21
? x 3 = 27	? x 1 = 10	6 x ? = 30	? x 5 = 45

Keep a record of your times for each test here

Do one test a day.

Date	Time	Date	Time	Date	Time	Date	Time

You may wish to cut out or photocopy this certificate for your bedroom wall.

Certificate

This is to certify that _____

knows the **x0, x1, x2, x3, x4, x5** and **x10** tables.

Signed by _____ , a responsible adult   Date _____

25

The Times Tables

x0 Table

1 x 0 = 0
2 x 0 = 0
3 x 0 = 0
4 x 0 = 0
5 x 0 = 0
6 x 0 = 0
7 x 0 = 0
8 x 0 = 0
9 x 0 = 0
10 x 0 = 0

x1 Table

1 x 1 = 1
2 x 1 = 2
3 x 1 = 3
4 x 1 = 4
5 x 1 = 5
6 x 1 = 6
7 x 1 = 7
8 x 1 = 8
9 x 1 = 9
10 x 1 = 10

x2 Table

1 x 2 = 2
2 x 2 = 4
3 x 2 = 6
4 x 2 = 8
5 x 2 = 10
6 x 2 = 12
7 x 2 = 14
8 x 2 = 16
9 x 2 = 18
10 x 2 = 20

x3 Table

1 x 3 = 3
2 x 3 = 6
3 x 3 = 9
4 x 3 = 12
5 x 3 = 15
6 x 3 = 18
7 x 3 = 21
8 x 3 = 24
9 x 3 = 27
10 x 3 = 30

x4 Table

1 x 4 = 4
2 x 4 = 8
3 x 4 = 12
4 x 4 = 16
5 x 4 = 20
6 x 4 = 24
7 x 4 = 28
8 x 4 = 32
9 x 4 = 36
10 x 4 = 40

x5 Table

1 x 5 = 5
2 x 5 = 10
3 x 5 = 15
4 x 5 = 20
5 x 5 = 25
6 x 5 = 30
7 x 5 = 35
8 x 5 = 40
9 x 5 = 45
10 x 5 = 50

x10 Table

1 x 10 = 10
2 x 10 = 20
3 x 10 = 30
4 x 10 = 40
5 x 10 = 50
6 x 10 = 60
7 x 10 = 70
8 x 10 = 80
9 x 10 = 90
10 x 10 = 100

The **x6, x7, x8, x9, x11** and **x12** tables are covered in **Times Tables Book 2.**

Schofield & Sims
HELPING CHILDREN TO LEARN

Schofield & Sims was established in 1901 by two headmasters and since then our name has been synonymous with educationally sound texts and teaching materials. Our mission is to publish products which are:

- Educationally sound • Good value • Written by experienced teachers
- Extensively used in schools, nurseries and play groups
- Used by parents to support their children's learning

TIMES TABLES BOOK 1

Straightforward tables practice through number grids, puzzles and tests. Removable answer booklet included in each book. Book 1 covers x0, x1, x2, x3, x4, x5, x10 tables. (Book 2 is for Key Stage 2)

Times Tables Book 1 - 0 7217 0811 0   **Times Tables Book 2 -** 0 7217 0812 9

Schofield & Sims Key Stage 1 products for 5 to 7 year olds

Language and literacy workbooks

Early Writing
Books 1 - 4
Training in letter formation, leading to joined-up writing.

Early Spellings
Books 1 - 3
Develops spelling skills through spelling activities, spelling patterns and establishing links between reading and writing.

Sound Practice
Books 1 - 5
Structured practice in basic sounds.

First Phonics
Books 1 - 4
Develops phonic skills through carefully graded enjoyable activities.

Basic Skills
Books 1 - 5
Helps children to achieve literacy and extend their vocabularies.

Maths and numeracy workbooks

Number Books
Books 1 - 5
Introduces basic number skills through gently graded activities.

Key Maths
Books 1 - 5
Graded maths activities for Key Stage 1.

Posters
Sturdy laminated posters, full colour, write-on/wipe-off, suitable for wall mounting or desk top use. Over 70 titles covering numeracy, literacy, days, time, shapes, seasons, weather, plus topics such as science, nature, geography, history and languages.

Schofield & Sims

Dogley Mill, Fenay Bridge, Huddersfield, HD8 0NQ
Phone 01484 607080   Fax 01484 606815
e-mail sales@schofieldandsims.co.uk

Information
For further information about products for pre-school, Key Stages 1 and 2, please request our catalogue or visit our website at
www.schofieldandsims.co.uk

ISBN 0-7217-0811-0

9 780721 708119

Price £1.95
Key Stage 1
Age Range 5 - 7 years